Reading Essentials in Social Studies

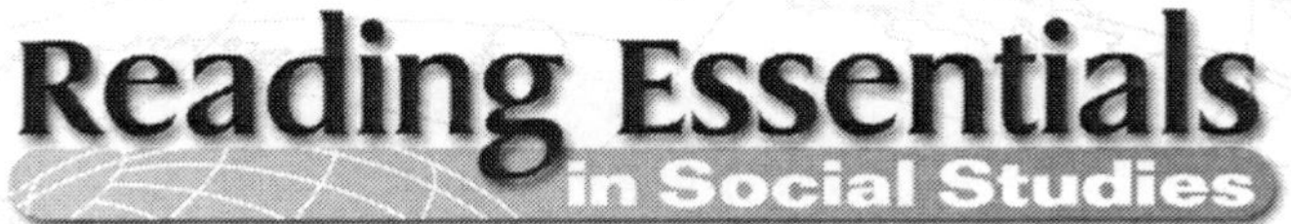

TEACHING AND ASSESSMENT RESOURCE

THE ANCIENT WORLD

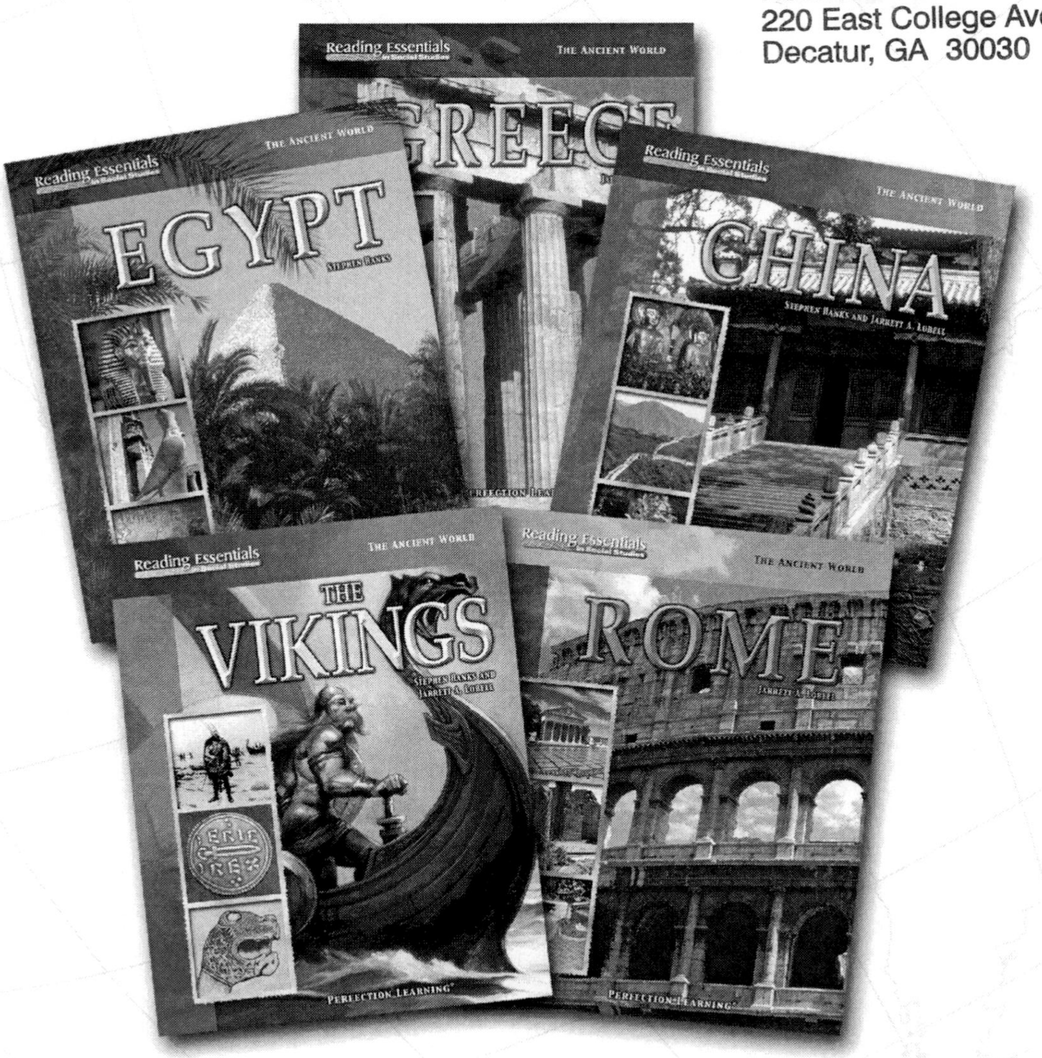

PERFECTION LEARNING®

Editorial Director: Susan C. Thies
Editor: Judith A. Bates
Writer: Traci Pedersen

Cover Design: Michael A. Aspengren
Book Design: Emily J. Greazel, Deborah Lea Bell, Gayle O'Brien

Image Credits: ArtToday (some images copyright www.arttoday.com): 5, 6, 7, 8, 9, 10, 16, 17, 21, 27, 32, 46, 53, 56, 58, 66

For information, contact
Perfection Learning® Corporation
1000 North Second Avenue, P.O. Box 500
Logan, Iowa 51546-0500.
Phone: 1-800-831-4190 • Fax: 1-800-543-2745
perfectionlearning.com
Printed in the United States of America

2 3 4 5 6 PP 07 08 06 05 04

ISBN 0-7891-5944-2

Table of Contents

Table of Contents *continued*

Reading Essentials in Social Studies

> " 'Begin at the beginning,' the king said gravely,
> 'and go till you come to the end; then stop.' "
> Lewis Carroll,
> *Alice's Adventures in Wonderland*, (1865), p. 12

Unfortunately, this is the way many learners read—from beginning to end—regardless of the reading task in front of them, whether it be reading for information or pleasure, expository or narrative. This passive, linear approach to text compromises understanding and reading success. Successful readers need to be actively involved in the reading process, monitoring their understanding, personally relating to the text, and applying what they know to understand what they're reading.

While active reading strategies are important to the comprehension of any type of reading material, they are especially important in understanding informational, or expository, text. It is estimated that about 90 percent of adult reading is to acquire information, while only about 10 percent is for pleasure. So content literacy skills will be important to students far beyond their school years. In their interactions with informational text, student readers should be learning content while developing the literacy and thinking skills necessary to become lifelong readers.

Reading Essentials in Social Studies helps readers learn more about concepts introduced in social studies and develop content literacy strategies. Few students ever develop a passion for reading from their social studies textbooks. The interesting, visually appealing, reader-friendly student books in *Reading Essentials in Social Studies* provide essential content and content-area reading practice as they pique students' interest. And the content literacy skills and strategies presented and practiced in the accompanying activities in the strand resources will prepare students for a lifetime of enjoyable and meaningful literacy experiences.

Overview of the Program

Reading Essentials in Social Studies offers curricular-aligned informational books for students in grades 3 to 6, strand resources for practice and assessment of content and content literacy strategies, and a program resource for teaching content literacy strategies.

Reading Essentials in Social Studies Student Books

The interesting and informative nonfiction titles are 40 to 48 pages in length and arranged in thematic strands with five related books per strand. The social studies strands are organized using the following disciplines: American History, Government, Geography, and World History.

Reading Essentials in Social Studies Teaching and Assessment Resources

The reproducible strand resources offer students opportunities to extend content knowledge and develop and practice content literacy strategies. Additionally, twenty-question objective tests and performance-based assessment suggestions are provided for each title to monitor student growth. These comprehensive resources have a separate section for each of the five titles in the strands.

Reading Essentials Strategies Resource

This collection of research-based content literacy strategies will help you make the best use of the student books and the practice and assessment activities in the strand resource.

Rationale: Why Teach Content-Area Reading?

Many mistakenly believe that students do not need further reading instruction once they learn to decode. However, reading goes beyond mere decoding. Content comprehension is dependent upon an active relationship between the reader and the text. Teaching reading in the content areas helps learners make connections between what they know and the new information in the text.

In order to develop content-area knowledge, students need interesting, relevant content-area books. Additionally, students need to develop and practice content-area strategies to learn to interact with the text and create meaning. Many readers have never been taught that they need to think when they are reading and to create pictures in their mind. Reading is not passive word calling. Readers who are not actively involved in their reading, who aren't monitoring their understanding by personally relating to the text and applying what they know to understand what they're reading, will finish with little or no understanding of what they've read. Often they lose confidence in themselves as readers, give up on reading, and fall behind.

The social studies titles and content-area literacy skills and strategies presented and practiced in the *Reading Essentials in Social Studies* program will help students learn how to learn, enabling them to acquire knowledge independently from their reading in school and throughout their lives.

The Ancient World

The Ancient World Student Books

The five titles in The Ancient World series are *China*, *Egypt*, *Greece*, *Rome*, and *The Vikings*. Each title offers information about the civilization's beginning—the history, the government, and the lifestyle. Each title features an index and a glossary. The content-specific vocabulary included in the glossary is bolded throughout the text. Additionally, Internet sites are provided to extend the information presented in the book.

The *Reading Essentials in Social Studies* Ancient World titles contain considerate text that is well organized and clearly written. In this way, readers are actively involved in their learning as they make connections and create meaning.

The Ancient World Teaching and Assessment Resource

This comprehensive resource covers all five titles in the strand. Each title-specific section offers

- a synopsis of the chapters in the student book
- reading exploration activities (prereading, during reading, and postreading)

  In order for students to understand the new information presented in the books, they need to relate what they're reading to what they already know. The prereading activities help learners call up prior knowledge and make connections to what they're learning. The during reading and postreading suggestions provide students with a purpose for reading and guide them in using active reading strategies.
- a content-specific vocabulary activity

  Research shows that vocabulary knowledge is one of the most important factors in increased comprehension.
- two reading skills activities

  Reading skills activities link essential reading skills and strategies with important content.

- a writing activity
  As students write, they make personal connections between the content and themselves.
- a content-area activity
  As students complete activities related to the content, they extend their subject matter knowledge.
- ten project suggestions
  The performance-based activities offer students alternative ways to extend their learning and/or demonstrate their understanding.
- a twenty-question objective test
  Objective assessment is presented in a format similar to the questions on state and standardized tests.

Second Language Learners

The terms English for Speakers of Other Languages (ESOL), English as a Second Language (ESL), or English Language Learners (ELL) were developed to recognize students whose heritage language is other than English. Classrooms today are comprised of a rich variety of heritages and languages reflecting the diverse cultural nature of our society. The Limited English Proficiency (LEP) students enter the classroom at various limited English language levels. They are faced with challenging content in an unfamiliar language. An appropriate instructional model must be in place for these students. ESOL instruction is designed to meet the needs of LEP students by providing instruction based on their level of English proficiency.

When developing and enriching instruction through ESOL strategies, the educator must be sensitive to the student's first language and cultural background while at the same time encouraging the student to acquire the English language in a nonthreatening and productive learning environment. The student's individual differences and learning styles must also be considered when applying ESOL strategies. All LEP students are entitled to equal educational opportunities that include access to materials, programs, and experiences.

Using Reading Essentials in Social Studies with Limited English Students

The *Reading Essentials in Social Studies* program offers LEP students an opportunity to learn grade-level content as they acquire proficiency in the English language. Through the use of certain instructional strategies, LEP students, representing a diverse group of language backgrounds and individual differences, can find success with the same books that are being enjoyed by their English-speaking classmates.

The use of graphic organizers is an effective ESOL strategy. Flow charts, pie charts, family trees, Venn diagrams, etc., are all appropriate and recommended. Additionally, cooperative learning groups offer support and nonthreatening learning environments for LEP students as they develop linguistic and academic skills.

The additional strategies shown below should be used at certain times throughout the lesson to help each student's individual language development and to help him or her progress to a proficient English language level.

Before Reading

Content-area vocabulary is provided on the inside front covers of all *Reading Essentials in Social Studies* titles. While all students benefit from the preteaching of content vocabulary, it is critical for LEP students. They cannot rely on context clues and general background knowledge to the extent their English-language peers can. Introduce the vocabulary in context and use picture cues with vocabulary definitions to ensure understanding.

Below are some specific strategies that will better prepare LEP students to access the core content information in *Reading Essentials in Social Studies*.

- Encourage communication in the classroom setting. LEP students learn so much by listening to their peers.
- Develop predictions based on cover art and book titles. Many of the *Reading Essentials in Social Studies* books include images that are recognizable to English-speaking students but won't be to LEP students. Make sure images and their relationship to the content are clearly explained.
- Use graphic organizers. Build webs around content vocabulary introduced to expand language acquisition and deepen understanding.
- Make the language comprehensible through the use of gestures, visuals, concrete examples, and oral communication.
- Use the suggested activities in this teacher resource to build background knowledge. Restate, expand, paraphrase, repeat, and speak clearly and slowly.

During Reading

The Reading Essentials in Social Studies books are filled with colorful, descriptive visuals. Use the graphics to create meaning for your students. Study and discuss the visuals as well as the text.

Additionally, the following specific strategies will help LEP students acquire the core knowledge presented in the *Reading Essentials in Social Studies* books.

- Continuously refer to the vocabulary in context.
- Draw on students' personal experiences to add meaning to the discussion.
- Provide for much discussion and encourage students to contribute through their thoughts, questions, and opinions.
- Allow oral and written responses to accommodate individual differences.
- Provide time for directed dialogue between student pairs and between teacher and student.

- Encourage journal writing: reflective, descriptive, and expository.
- Tape selections for students.
- Allow for an extended response time. LEP students need time to process their thoughts and responses in an unfamiliar language.

After Reading

In addition to the reading, writing, and content-area activities provided in this resource, use the following strategies with your LEP students to extend and assess the content information presented.

- Encourage students to express personal reactions through written, oral, or pictorial activities.
- Arrange students in cooperative groups to complete the reading, writing, and content-area activities.
- Provide students an opportunity to demonstrate their understanding through one of the project ideas.
- Offer students a chance to complete the twenty-question objective test orally rather than in writing.

Skills and Strategies Chart

The Ancient World

The following chart shows the essential reading, writing, vocabulary, speaking, listening, and viewing skills presented and practiced in the activities in The Ancient World Resource.

Reading Essentials	China	Egypt	Greece	Rome	Vikings
Analyzing Information	✔		✔		✔
Comparing and Contrasting	✔				✔
Determining Cause & Effect				✔	
Distinguishing Fact & Fiction	✔				
Distinguishing Fact & Opinion				✔	
Drawing Conclusions				✔	
Evaluating	✔	✔	✔		✔
Identifying Time Order			✔		
Making Inferences					✔
Reading and Using a Map	✔	✔	✔	✔	✔
Reading Charts & Graphs				✔	
Recalling Facts	✔	✔		✔	
Recognizing Main Idea & Details			✔		✔
Sequencing			✔		
Using Prereading Strategies	✔	✔	✔	✔	✔
Writing Essentials					
Researching		✔	✔	✔	✔
Making an Outline			✔		
Using the Writing Process	✔				
Writing a Friendly Letter				✔	
Writing to Describe		✔		✔	
Writing to Entertain	✔			✔	✔
Writing to Inform		✔		✔	
Writing to Persuade			✔		
Writing to Summarize		✔	✔		✔
Vocabulary Essentials					
Alphabetizing					✔
Building Content-Area Vocabulary	✔	✔	✔	✔	✔
Identifying Parts of Speech		✔			
Understanding Synonyms & Antonyms			✔		
Using a Glossary	✔		✔	✔	✔
Using Context Clues		✔		✔	
Speaking, Listening, and Viewing Essentials					
Speaking to Entertain				✔	
Speaking to Inform	✔	✔			✔
Speaking to Persuade			✔		
Visual Literacy	✔	✔	✔	✔	✔

National Social Studies Standards Correlation

The following chart lists the ten themes as determined by the National Council of Social Studies that form the framework for the teaching of social studies at grades K–12. The content within the five books in The Ancient World strand in *Reading Essentials in Social Studies* supports the national standards as shown below.

Theme	Standards
I. Culture	Compare similarities and differences in the ways groups, societies, and cultures meet human needs and concerns. Explain and give examples of how language, literature, the arts, architecture, other artifacts, traditions, beliefs, values, and behaviors contribute to the development and transmission of culture. Explain why individuals and groups respond differently to their physical and social environments and/or changes to them on the basis of shared assumptions, values, and beliefs.
II. Time, Continuity, and Change	Identify and use key concepts such as chronology, causality, change, conflict, and complexity to explain, analyze, and show connections among patterns of historical change and continuity. Identify and describe selected historical periods and patterns of change within and across cultures, such as the rise of civilizations, the development of transportation systems, the growth and breakdown of colonial systems, and others. Identify and use processes important to reconstructing and reinterpreting the past, such as using a variety of sources, providing, validating, and weighing evidence for claims, checking credibility of sources, and searching for causality. Develop critical sensitivities such as empathy and skepticism regarding attitudes, values, and behaviors of people in different historical contexts. Use knowledge of facts and concepts drawn from history, along with methods of historical inquiry, to inform decision-making about and action taking on public issues.
III. People, Places, and Environments	Elaborate mental maps of locales, regions, and the world that demonstrate understanding of relative location, direction, size, and shape. Create, interpret, use, and distinguish various representations of the earth, such as maps, globes, and photographs. Describe ways that historical events have been influenced by, and have influenced, physical and human geographic factors in local, regional, national, and global settings.

IV. Individual Development and Identity	Describe personal connections to place—as associated with community, nation, and world. Relate personal changes to social, cultural, and historical contexts. Identify and describe the influence of perception, attitudes, values, and beliefs on personal identity.
V. Individuals, Groups, and Institutions	Demonstrate an understanding of concepts such as roles, status, and social class in describing the interactions of individuals and social groups. Analyze group and institutional influences on people, events, and elements of culture. Describe the various forms institutions take and the interactions of people with institutions. Identify and analyze examples of tensions between expressions of individuality and group or institutional efforts to promote social conformity. Identify and describe examples of tensions between belief systems and government policies and laws. Describe the role of institutions in furthering both continuity and change.
VI. Power, Authority, and Governance	Examine persistent issues involving the rights, roles, and status of the individual in relation to the general welfare. Describe the purpose of government and how its powers are acquired, used, and justified. Analyze and explain ideas and governmental mechanisms to meet needs and wants of citizens, regulate territory, manage conflict, and establish order and security. Identify and describe the basic features of the political system in the United States, and identify representative leaders from various levels and branches of government. Give examples and explain how governments attempt to achieve their stated ideals at home and abroad.

VII. Production, Distribution, and Consumption	Give and explain examples of ways that economic systems structure choices about how goods and services are to be produced and distributed. Explain and illustrate how values and beliefs influence different economic decisions. Compare basic economic systems according to who determines what is produced, distributed, and consumed. Use economic concepts to help explain historical and current developments and issues in local, national, or global contexts.
VIII. Science, Technology, and Society	Describe examples in which values, beliefs, and attitudes have been influenced by new scientific and technological knowledge, such as the invention of the printing press, conceptions of the universe, applications of atomic energy, and genetic discoveries.
IX. Global Connections	Analyze examples of conflict, cooperation, and interdependence among groups, societies, and nations. Demonstrate understanding of concerns, standards, issues, and conflicts related to universal human rights. Identify and describe the roles of international and multinational organizations.
X. Civic Ideals and Practice	Examine the origins and continuing influence of key ideals of the democratic republican form of government, such as individual human dignity, liberty, justice, equality, and the rule of law. Identify and interpret sources and examples of the rights and responsibilities of citizens. Explain and analyze various forms of citizen action that influence public policy decisions.

China
in Brief

Chapter 1 highlights the governmental history of ancient China. China endured various dynasties, empires, and rulers during the years between 1776 B.C. and 1325 A.D. Some of these empires brought peace and prosperity while others fostered oppression and war.

Marco Polo is introduced in this chapter as well. He and his family traveled from Italy to China along the Silk Road. Needing a rest at the end of their 3½-year journey, the Polos decided to stay in China. They resided in Emperor Kublai Khan's court for 17 years, acquiring great wealth and knowledge of Chinese inventions. Polo became famous for his written accounts of his incredible adventures.

Chapter 2 explores the daily life of the ancient Chinese people. For thousands of years, farming was the center of society. Ancient farmers grew crops for themselves, the city, and the army.

The peasants and the wealthy were distinguished by the food they ate, the clothes they wore, and the homes in which they lived. Many generations lived under one roof, and family pride and honor were of extreme importance in ancient China.

The earliest traces of Chinese writing, called the Oracle Bone inscriptions, date back to 1200 B.C. Other ancient writings have been found on vessels and tablets and later on bamboo strips. Documents have been found that record rituals, remedies, philosophies, poetry, and the ancient Chinese calendar.

Chapter 3 reveals the different religions of ancient China. There are five major religions or philosophies in China today, all which have ancient roots. These include the philosophies of Confucianism and Taoism and the religions of Buddhism, Islam, and Christianity. Mythology also has a place in Chinese history. Stories of gods, heroes, and ghosts were popular in ancient China.

Chapter 4 emphasizes the leadership of Shihuangdi, Emperor of the ancient Qin territory. This small state eventually conquered all of the surrounding areas, and China became a unified land. Extensive building projects, including the Great Wall of China, were built under Shihuangdi, yet he was an unpopular Emperor because of his harsh leadership.

Chapter 5 takes a specific look at the longest structure in the world, the Great Wall of China. The building of this wall began 2,000 years ago and was a connection and extension of smaller walls. The Great Wall protected China for thousands of years against invaders.

Another large structure, the Great Buddha of Leshan, is noted in chapter 5. At 234 feet tall and 83 feet wide at the shoulders, this Buddha was carved in the hopes that it would protect travelers in the dangerous rivers below.

Chapter 6 introduces the great inventions of the ancient Chinese, including silk, gunpowder, tea, and paper.

The Chinese made great contributions in the areas of science and technology. By the 3rd century A.D., scientists had discovered magnets, which led to the creation of the first compass. They also created the first seismograph and the first abacus.

Reading Exploration Essentials

Vocabulary

artisan	astronomical	divination	dynasty
Eurasia	feudal state	heir apparent	Huns
imperialism	irrigation	legacy	Mohism
nomad	terrace		

Reading Exploration

prereading

Ask students to share what they already know about ancient China. You may prompt them with the following questions.

- Did the Chinese invent anything we use today? (silk, tea, gunpowder, paper, compass)
- Are there any well-known structures in China? (Great Wall of China, Great Buddha of Leshan)
- What religions or philosophies are practiced in China? (Buddhism, Confucianism, Taoism, Islam, and Christianity)

Set up a map of China. Discuss how several different empires and dynasties ruled ancient China for thousands of years until it became unified in 221 B.C.

postreading

Ask students to share what they've learned about ancient China. Have them compare ancient China with what they know about China today. Would they like to visit China today? Why or why not?

Name ______________________________

Ancient Chinese Secrets

Unscramble the following glossary words. Match each final word to its correct definition. Use the glossary in *China* if you need help.

1. ______ynysatd	a. act of supplying land with water by artificial means
2. ______snuh	b. something left after one dies
3. ______graitinior	c. ruling family that passes control from one family to the next
4. ______doman	d. person with no fixed home who wanders from place to place
5. ______eyglac	e. nomadic people who originated in north-central Asia and invaded China in 3rd century B.C.
6. ______sitrana	f. person who works at a trade requiring skill with

◎ **One Step Further:** Find three new words in the text or the glossary of China and scramble them! See if your classmates can figure them out and give definitions.

1. ______________________________
2. ______________________________
3. ______________________________

Name ______________________________

Rich Man, Poor Man

As in any culture, life was different for the poor and the wealthy of ancient China. Review Chapter 2 in *China*. Compare the diets, clothing, and housing of the poor and wealthy. Record your findings in the chart below.

	Poor	Wealthy
Diets		
Clothing		
Housing		

What other differences or similarities were there between the lifestyles of the poor and the wealthy in ancient China?

____

____

____

____

____

____

____

____

____

____

Name ______________________________

Chinese Fiction

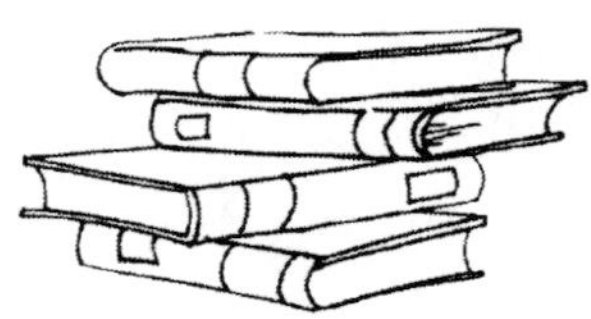

A nonfiction book contains a true story or real information. A fiction book is an invented story.

There are both nonfiction and fiction books on nearly every topic. After reading the nonfiction book *China*, you've probably learned a lot about the country's ancient culture.

Now try fiction! Check your school or local library for a fiction book or short story that has an ancient Chinese setting or Chinese characters. Ask your media specialist to suggest titles. If you can't find a book with an ancient theme, you could read a present-day book instead. It could be a picture book or a chapter book. It could be true-to-life or completely unrealistic. Choose the one that strikes you as the most interesting. Enjoy!

Chinese Fiction Book Title______________________________

Type of Fiction (Circle One) True-to-Life Unrealistic

Main Characters

__________ __________ __________

__________ __________ __________

Setting

____

____

What made you choose this particular book? How is it different from the nonfiction book *China*? Would you recommend it to others? Why or why not?

____

____

____

____

____

____

____

Name ________________________________

A Second Chance

It's hard to write something perfectly the first time. It helps to write a rough draft first, edit and revise, and then write your final draft. Using your new knowledge of ancient China, write a short story, tale, or myth.

Check your first draft for misspellings, capitalization and punctuation errors, and unclear words or sentences. Make any corrections with a red pen. Rewrite your story on another sheet of paper after all corrections have been made.

First Draft

____

____

____

____

____

____

____

____

____

____

____

____

____

____

____

____

____

____

____

Name ______________________________

An Invention That Counts

The ancient Chinese were both creative and practical inventors. Their invention of the abacus made it easier to count to higher numbers. This is a fairly simple device featuring beads strung onto wires. The beads are moved across to represent units: tens, hundreds, and thousands. The abacus is still used today.

Make your own abacus using creative materials. It may be similar to the ancient Chinese abacus, or it may be a completely unique model. Display your final product and be ready to explain and demonstrate how it works.

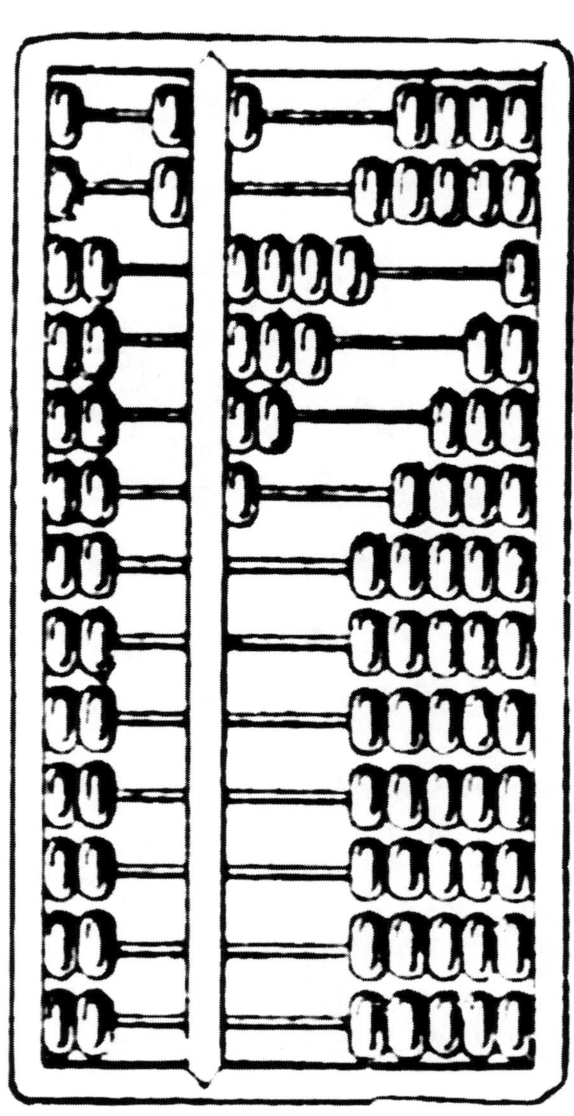

Project Ideas

Choose from the following project suggestions to show what you've learned about ancient China. You may want to work with a partner or in a small group. Share your finished project with your classmates.

- Make a chart listing the various ancient empires and dynasties in China. Include the years they ruled and their accomplishments or failures.
- Under the Tang emperors of China (618–907 A.D.), culture blossomed. Write a poem describing life during these years.
- Read more about Marco Polo and the adventures he had. Then give an oral presentation of these adventures from his point of view.
- Create a model of Shihuangdi's burial tomb with his terra-cotta army.
- A favorite ancient Chinese game was the tangram, in which pictures were made from seven different shapes that had been cut from a square. (See page 17 of *China*.) These seven shapes have traditionally been five triangles, a parallelogram, and a square, although more shapes can be added for difficulty. Make your own tangram and see how many pictures you can create with it. Make a display in your classroom. Visit **http://www.careergroup.com/chinesetangrams.html** for some possibilities.
- Calligraphy is a popular art form in China. Research Chinese calligraphy. Then create your own calligraphy using Chinese characters.
- Plan a virtual trip to China to visit the Great Wall. What sections of the wall will you see? What else will you visit while you're there? Where will you stay? How long will you remain in China? Make a scrapbook of your trip.
- Write your own ancient Chinese myth. Create a picture to display with your story.
- Research how silk is produced. Create an illustrated chart or other type of display showing the steps from beginning to end. If possible, include sample swatches of silk in your display.
- Make a map of ancient China. Use transparency paper to create overlays to show different periods in China's history. Remember to include cities and locations of famous structures.

Name ______________________________

Twenty-Question Objective Test

Directions: Match each word and its meaning.

______ 1. irrigation

______ 2. imperialism

______ 3. dynasty

______ 4. heir apparent

______ 5. terrace

a. form of government ruled by an emperor

b. person who has legal claim to a title or throne after the holder dies

c. act of supplying land with water by artificial means

d. raised embankment with a leveled top

e. ruling family that passes control from one member to the next

---

Directions: Answer each statement True (T) or False (F).

______ 6. The Chinese bought silk from the Europeans.

______ 7. The Sui emperors introduced a system of electing officials.

______ 8. Marco Polo and his family stayed in Kublai Khan's court for 17 years.

______ 9. Chou is probably where the name China originated.

______ 10. Confucius was a great emperor.

Directions: Choose the best answer to complete each statement.

11. Ying Zheng, the first emperor of China, changed his name to
   a. Yang Ti.
   b. Shihuangdi.
   c. Genghis Khan.

12. In 1325 A.D., a great famine created a death toll as high as
   a. 8 million.
   b. 10 million.
   c. 12 million.

continued

Name ____________________

China

Twenty-Question Objective Test continued

13. The Silk Road was the
    a. way to inner peace.
    b. most important trade route in the world.
    c. path from the emperor's home to the city.

14. The last Han emperor was forced to resign after the uprising called the
    a. Rebellion of the Blue Turbans.
    b. Rebellion of the Red Turbans.
    c. Rebellion of the Yellow Turbans.

15. The strong bond that held Chinese society together was
    a. family pride and honor.
    b. love of the emperor.
    c. gender equality.

16. The oldest Chinese writings are the
    a. bamboo strip inscriptions.
    b. Oracle Bone inscriptions.
    c. Anyang inscriptions.

17. The ancient Chinese calendar was based on
    a. the phases of the moon.
    b. the seasons.
    c. the position of the North Star.

18. The two philosophies developed within China are
    a. Christianity and Buddhism.
    b. Islam and Taoism.
    c. Confucianism and Taoism.

19. Shihuangdi had a burial tomb which included
    a. 6,000 terra-cotta soldiers.
    b. the Great Wall.
    c. canals for irrigation.

continued

Name ______________________________

China

Twenty-Question Objective Test continued

Directions: Answer the question using complete sentences.

20. Why was Shihuangdi so unpopular with the people?

Egypt in Brief

Chapter 1 of *Egypt* reveals the day-to-day life of this ancient civilization. The banks along the Nile River were extremely fertile and most Egyptians lived and worked on this land. Fishing, farming, and hunting were common occupations.

The Egyptians were inventors. They created the world's first paper and developed an intricate written language. They played instruments and transformed the three-string harp into a twenty-string instrument. Homes were constructed of mud bricks and situated on platforms to avoid the yearly flooding of the Nile River.

Chapter 2 explores the most monumental creation of the ancient Egyptians—the Great Pyramids. These pyramids were extravagant tombs for deceased pharaohs. The Egyptians believed that these structures would both protect the entombed pharaoh and help him reach the afterlife.

Chapter 3 introduces the Great Sphinx. This fascinating structure still sits in Giza at 66 feet tall and 241 feet long. The pharaoh, Khafre, ordered the half-man, half-lion structure built with the intention of having it guard over his own soul in the afterlife. Today, archaeologists are constantly restoring eroded parts and looking for ways to preserve this historical monument.

Chapter 4 recounts the lives of three of the most famous rulers of Egypt—Rameses the Great, King Tutankhamen, and Cleopatra.

Rameses the Great was the second of 11 rulers during Egypt's New Kingdom period. Rameses is remembered as a great builder. He frequently celebrated a war victory by erecting temples or statues of himself.

Tutankhamen, better known as King Tut, became pharaoh at age 9. He suddenly died at only 18 years of age. Many believe he was murdered since X rays show a significant head injury.

Cleopatra is the most famous queen in history. She ruled Egypt along with her half-brother, Ptolemy XIII. Power struggles caused her to flee the country, and her life eventually ended tragically by suicide.

Chapter 5 emphasizes two of the more infamous pharaohs of ancient Egypt—Hatshepsut and Akhenaten. After Queen Hatshepsut's husband, Tuthmosis II, died, she crowned herself pharaoh until Tuthmosis III was old enough to take over the throne. She even posed as a man when she visited other countries.

King Akhenaten believed in the worship of only one god at a time when polytheism was commonplace. The god of choice was the little-known god called the Aten. After Akhenaten's death, priests and advisors tried to eliminate all evidence of Akhenaten's existence.

Chapter 6 reveals the religion of ancient Egypt. The Egyptians worshiped many gods, each of whom had distinct powers and characteristics. This chapter features the details of ten of these ancient Egyptian gods.

Chapter 7 features ancient Egyptian mummies as well as the process of mummification. The Egyptians wanted to preserve the bodies of their dead so they could make it to the afterlife. Animals were also mummified. Some were placed in the tombs to keep their owners company.

Many mummies have been recovered and can be seen in museums around the world. These reveal a glimpse into the fascinating culture of ancient Egypt.

Reading Exploration Essentials

Vocabulary

archaeologist	avenging	Book of the Dead	canopic jar
dynasty	Egyptologist	Great Pyramid	hieroglyphs
ibis	inscription	loincloth	mastaba
millennia	mummy	myrrh	Nile River
obelisk	papyrus	pharaoh	sarcophagus
scribe	sphinx	stele	

Reading Exploration

prereading

Have students locate Egypt on a classroom map or globe. Ask them to list at least five words that come to mind when the country of Egypt is mentioned.

Have students raise their hands if they listed any of the following.

- the Nile River
- hieroglyphics
- the pyramids
- the Sphinx
- pharaoh
- mummies

Explain that most of the things we know about Egypt today were developed, or were an important part of life, during ancient history.

Now have them read through the chapter titles of *Egypt*. Ask students which chapter they look most forward to reading. Promote a lively discussion among the students to whet their appetites for Egypt.

during and postreading

Have students write any questions they might have as they read *Egypt*. When they have completed the book, compile the questions on chart paper. Encourage each student to choose a question, and with a partner, research the answer. Have students share their findings with the class.

Name ______________________________

Egypt

The Whole Story

The story below is missing some important words! Use what you know about the following vocabulary words to fill in the blanks. You may double-check the definitions in *Egypt's* glossary.

archaeologist	canopic jar	Egyptologist
hieroglyphics	pharaoh	Nile River
mummy	sarcophagus	stele

Emily's favorite subject in school is science. She especially enjoyed the recent field trip her class took to the museum. They had visited to learn about Egyptian culture and see some relics of ancient Egypt. First, the museum guide spoke of the (1) ____________________ and its fertile banks.

Next the class got to see a limestone (2) ____________________ that had been found inside a tomb. It had (3) ____________________ inscribed on it. They looked like little pictures and symbols, and Emily had no idea what they meant. The guide said that these pictures told what the dead man enjoyed while he was still alive.

Emily almost fell over when she saw the (4) ____________________. It had been a real person who lived in ancient times. He had probably been a (5) ____________________. He was all wrapped up in linen, and he lay in a (6) ____________________. The guide said that the dead man's internal organs had been put into a (7) ____________________ when he died. Then the guide pulled the jar off a shelf! All the kids screamed even though it was empty.

After the field trip, Emily decided that she wanted to study to be an (8) ____________________. Who knows? Maybe when she grows up she'll specialize and become an (9) ____________________. Then she would give her findings to the museum for other kids to see!

◎ **One Step Further:** Now write your own story using five words from the glossary of *Egypt*.

Name ____________________

Extra! Extra! Read All About It!

Do you like the pyramids? mummies? pharaohs? So much literature has been written on ancient Egypt. Check out and read a library book on your favorite Egyptian subject. Then summarize your book below. Tell about the following.

- What is the title of your book?
- Who is the author?
- What is the genre, such as fiction, nonfiction, or biography?
- What or who is it about?
- If fiction, tell about the characters, setting, and plot.
- Did you or did you not like it?

Name ______________________________

Egypt

The Memory of an Elephant

Being able to recall information from a book you've read shows that you paid attention to and understood the text. See if you can remember what you've read about ancient Egypt by answering the questions below. You can check *Egypt* if you need a little help! Use complete sentences.

1. What kinds of foods did the ancient Egyptians eat? ______________________________

____

____

2. What are hieroglyphics? ______________________________

____

____

3. What kinds of toys did Egyptian children play with in ancient times? ______________

____

____

4. Why did the Egyptians build the pyramids? ______________________________

____

____

5. What was unusual about King Tut? ______________________________

____

____

◎ **One Step Further:** Think of a good question about ancient Egypt. Then pass it along to a friend.

Question: ______________________________

____

____

Name ____________________

Actions Speak Louder Than Being Verbs

There were so many interesting people and things in ancient Egypt. Writers can bring these characters to life by using descriptive or powerful words.

Which sentence is more descriptive?

- The pharaoh was upset with his advisor.
- The pharaoh snapped an irritated look at his annoying advisor.

Revise and expand the weak sentences below into more descriptive ones. Use action verbs and descriptive adjectives.

1. Cleopatra was sad. ____________________

2. Figs are tasty. ____________________

3. The pyramid is big. ____________________

4. Mummies are spooky. ____________________

5. Hieroglyphics are difficult to read. ____________________

◎ **One Step Further:** Write a descriptive paragraph about your favorite Egyptian subject. Share it with your classmates.

Name ___________________________________

Build a Pyramid

The ancient Egyptians built over 80 pyramids. Read again about the different pyramids listed in *Egypt*. Now construct your own pyramid! Keep it similar to the pyramids of old but be creative with your materials. Display your pyramid for your classmates to see. Give a talk or write a short paragraph describing the type of pyramid you constructed and the history of that type of pyramid.

You can check out books about pyramids from your school or local library. You can also try the Internet. The following Web sites might give you some good ideas.

http://www.historyforkids.org/learn/egypt/architecture/pyramids.htm—Displays pictures and descriptions of various kinds of pyramids.

http://www.ancientegypt.co.uk/pyramids/home.html—Gives details of different types of ancient Egyptian architecture.

Name ______________________________

Project Ideas

Choose from the following project suggestions to show what you've learned about ancient Egypt. You may want to work with a partner or in a small group. Share your finished project with your classmates.

- Hieroglyphics is a written language in which pictures represent words. Tell a story on a poster board using your own hieroglyphics!
- The Nile River was the "life-source" for the ancient Egyptians in many ways. But how does it help modern-day Egyptians? Research the benefits the Nile brings today. Then make a chart comparing what the Nile did for the ancient Egyptians with what it does for people today.
- Create a map of Egypt, pinpointing the locations of major cities, pyramids, the Nile, and the Sphinx. Also show the surrounding countries and bodies of water.
- The Great Sphinx of Egypt stands 66 feet tall and 241 feet long. Using a reduced scale of these dimensions, create a clay model of the Sphinx.
- King Tut became pharaoh at age nine. Imagine that you have just become a pharaoh. Prepare and present a speech for your loyal subjects (classmates). Tell them of the great things you have planned for the country. Persuade them to support your efforts.
- Write a short report about one of the famous pharaohs of ancient Egypt. Tell about some famous accomplishments, any mistakes made, likes/dislikes, and any unique characteristics.
- Research the building of the pyramids. Then give a demonstration showing how the ancient Egyptians moved the blocks of stone from the quarry and used ramps to slide the heavy blocks up to the tops of the pyramids.
- Write a ballad explaining how a particular farmer feels when the Nile overflows. Is he happy or sad? Does he feel blessed or cursed? Create artwork to go with your poem.
- Research the pharaohs of ancient Egypt. Create a timeline showing when each pharaoh reigned. Then write a short paragraph about which pharaoh you think was Egypt's most or least successful. Explain why you think so.
- Take a virtual trip to the Egyptian Museum in Cairo. Use this link to get there. **http://homepage.powerup.com.au/~ancient/museum.htm**. Write about your experience. Draw a picture of your favorite relic displayed at the museum.

Name ________________________________

Twenty-Question Objective Test

Directions: Match each word and its meaning.

______ 1.	mastaba	a.	four-sided pillar that tapers toward the top and ends in a pyramid
______ 2.	obelisk	b.	an oblong Egyptian tomb with sloping sides and a flat roof
______ 3.	myrrh	c.	stone slab decorated with carvings and inscriptions
______ 4.	stele	d.	brown, slightly bitter, fragrant material used in perfume and incense
______ 5.	sarcophagus	e.	container or coffin used to hold the mummy of an ancient Egyptian

---

Directions: Answer each statement True (T) or False (F).

______ 6. Egypt lies on the northwestern coast of Africa.

______ 7. Egyptians often went barefoot.

______ 8. Both boys and girls attended school.

______ 9. *Hieroglyphic* is a Greek word meaning "sacred carving."

______ 10. Khufu's pyramid was the largest of the Great Pyramids of Giza.

Directions: Choose the best answer to complete each statement.

11. Ancient Egyptians ate with
    a. crude versions of forks and knives.
    b. their fingers.
    c. chopsticks.

12. The ancient Egyptians transformed the three-string harp into
    a. a twenty-string harp.
    b. a guitar.
    c. a violin.

continued

Name ______________________

Egypt

Twenty-Question Objective Test continued

13. An early form of Egyptian checkers was played on something similar to
    a. hopscotch squares.
    b. a tic-tac-toe board.
    c. today's checkerboard.

14. The pyramids were intended to be
    a. houses for social events.
    b. places of worship.
    c. tombs for pharaohs.

15. The pyramids of ancient Egypt were most likely built by
    a. pharoahs and advisors.
    b. slaves and prisoners.
    c. stone masons and sculptors.

16. Most Egyptologists believe the Great Pyramids are no more than
    a. 5,000 years old.
    b. 3,000 years old.
    c. 1,500 years old.

17. The Sphinx was intended to guard over
    a. all Egyptians.
    b. King Khafre's soul.
    c. the crops.

18. Rameses II was married to
    a. Nefertari.
    b. Cleopatra.
    c. Hatshepsut.

19. Hathor was considered the goddess of
    a. childbirth.
    b. dance, music, and love.
    c. peace and justice.

continued

Name ____________________

Egypt

Twenty-Question Objective Test continued

Directions: Answer the question using complete sentences.

20. Why are the ancient Egyptian pyramids considered so amazing?

Greece
in Brief

Chapter 1 of *Greece* highlights the unique civilizations and rulers that influenced the history of this ancient land. The specific Greek periods of peace, war, confusion, and expansion are detailed, and influential Greek people are introduced, including rulers, politicians, playwrights, and historians.

The famous Trojan War is also discussed as well as the controversial excavations of the famous city of Troy.

Chapter 2 emphasizes the rise and fall of Athens, a great city-state in ancient Greece. This area was the center of the Greek world for thousands of years. After Athens defeated the Persians in the Battle of Marathon, the people established the Delian League. This was an important alliance of city-states to protect Greece from the Persians. Athens eventually controlled the more than 200 city-states in the Delian League.

Eventually, Sparta defeated Athens in the Peloponnesian War. Just as Greece began to renew itself, it fell to King Philip II of Macedonia. Athens eventually became part of a Roman province.

Pericles, the greatest builder in Greek history, is also introduced along with his famous architecture.

Chapter 3 records the daily life of those living in ancient Greece. Housing differed by region and the owner's economic and social status. One's diet also depended upon economic position. Only the wealthiest could afford meat. The two most important fruit crops for everyone were grapes for wine and olives for oil.

Only male children, except for the poorest, were allowed to attend school. All Greek women learned to spin yarn, weave cloth, and take care of house and family. Writing was an important part of Greek life. Ancient Greek literature is some of the finest in world history.

Chapter 4 emphasizes the religion of ancient Greece, which was based on myths and included the worship of gods and goddesses. A system of rituals was designed to keep in constant communication with the gods. These included the wearing of special clothing, saying prayers, cleansing and purifying the body, burning incense, and making offerings.

Chapter 5 explores entertainment in ancient Greece. Hospitality was an important concept, and feasts with exotic foods and a lot of wine were often enjoyed. Festivals were an opportunity for the Greeks to honor their gods and heroes, to honor young men and women in their rite of passage to adulthood, to honor the dead, and to simply have fun.

The Olympic Games were the most famous entertainment. The sports included horse racing, boxing, wrestling, running, chariot racing, and the pentathlon. Much is known about the Olympics from illustrated vases and ancient written descriptions of the Games.

The theater was also very popular in ancient Greece. An annual playwright competition was held during the Festival of Dionysis in Athens. The winner of this contest was greatly respected.

Chapter 6 explains the process of dating Greek artifacts through the study of ancient pottery. The different types of pottery created by separate Greek civilizations give a glimpse into what was a changing culture and diverse land.

Reading Exploration Essentials

Vocabulary

alliance	Amazons	archaeologist	archenemy	aristocrat
artifact	artisan	chronology	decipher	deity
divination	dominant	epic	fortified	frieze
Koran	legume	libation	minotaur	mosaic
offering	ointment	philosophy	pictograph	pillage
plague	playwright	potsherd	province	satyr–play
shrine	tyrant			

Reading Exploration

prereading

Display a classroom world map. Explain that at different time periods, ancient Greece included various areas of Europe, Asia Minor, and even Africa. Maps of ancient Greece can be found at the following Web site.

http://library.thinkquest.org/10805/map-g.html

Preview the main periods of Greek civilization. These include the following.

- Bronze Age—Cycladic, Minoan, and Mycenaean cultures develop in the Aegean Sea area.
- Dark Ages—Little is known of this time period.
- Archaic Period—Greeks increase power and found new colonies in Mediterranean.
- Classical Period/Golden Age—The Delian League is founded. This is an alliance of Greek cities with Athens as most powerful. Architecture, art, philosophy, and literature flourish.
- Period of confusion—Athens experiences several rulers until Alexander the Great takes over.
- Hellenistic Period—Greek influence permeates throughout Alexander the Great's empire after his death. Outstanding advances are made in technology, architecture, philosophy, and medicine.
- Rome takes control of Greece.

Ask students the following questions.

- Why do you think the arts and sciences prospered in certain periods?
- Why do you think we know so little about the Dark Ages?

postreading

Lead students in a discussion of how contributions from Greek architecture, art, philosophy, science, and literature have affected the modern world.

Name ____________________

Word Exchange

Synonyms are words that share the same meaning. Listed below are vocabulary words from *Greece*. Look up their definitions in the glossary of your book. Then think of a synonym for each word that could logically take its place in the sentence. Your synonym may be more than one word.

The part of speech is given after each term. Any verb tenses may be changed. You may use a dictionary or thesaurus. An example is provided.

Example: pictograph (n); The Minoans developed a system of writing based on <u>pictures</u> that stood for words.

1. alliance (n.); A(n) ____________________ was formed between Greek cities called the Delian League.

2. province (n.); Greece eventually became the Roman ____________________ of Macedonia.

3. aristocrats (n.); Under Roman rule, control of Macedonia was given to wealthy ____________________.

4. epic (adj.); The *Iliad* and the *Odyssey* are two ____________________ poems.

5. decipher (v.); In 1952, Michael Ventris was able to ____________________ the ancient Greek language.

6. dominant (adj.); Christianity eventually became the ____________________ religion of the Roman Empire.

7. artisans (n.); Skilled ____________________ built the Propylea and decorated it with statues.

8. artifacts (n.); We know much about the ancient Greek language from ____________________.

continued

Word Exchange *continued*

9. pillaged (v.); Violent tribes __________________ a weakened Greece, ending its ancient world.

10. fortified (adj.); The Mycenaeans built enormous, __________________ palaces.

◎ **One Step Further:** Write your own sentence using one or more of these vocabulary words. Then rewrite your sentence by replacing each vocabulary word with a synonym. Did the meaning of the sentence change or stay the same?

____

____

____

____

____

____

____

____

____

Name ______________________________

History in a Nutshell

Each of the significant events that shaped and influenced ancient Greece occurred in a specific time period. Reread *Greece* to find the year, or series of years, in which the following events occurred. List the dates to the left of each event. Then place the number of each event under its specific time period in the chart on page 42.

______________________ 1. The Peloponnesian War between Athens and Sparta begins.

______________________ 2. The Persian Empire, which becomes one of Greece's greatest rivals, is founded.

______________________ 3. Minoan civilization flourishes and expands across much of Greece.

______________________ 4. The Delian League is formed.

______________________ 5. Philip II of Macedonia defeats the Greeks at the Battle of Chaeronea.

______________________ 6. Red-figure vase painting is invented.

______________________ 7. Peisistratus seizes power and makes himself tyrant of Athens.

______________________ 8. The city of Troy is destroyed.

______________________ 9. Greece becomes the Roman province of Macedonia.

______________________ 10. First Olympic Games are held in Olympia.

______________________ 11. Cleisthenes divides people into tribes based on politics.

______________________ 12. Mycenaeans invade mainland Greece from the north.

continued

Name ______________________________

History in a Nutshell *continued*

______________ 13. The Phoenicians develop an alphabet that will later become the source of the Greek alphabet.

______________ 14. Athens wins a great victory over the Persians at the Battle of Marathon.

______________ 15. Pericles builds the Parthenon.

Time Periods				
Bronze Age 3000–1200 B.C.	Dark Ages 1200–750 B.C.	Archaic Period 750–500 B.C.	Classical Period 500–323 B.C.	Hellenistic Period 323–31 B.C.

Name ______________________________

Support or Oppose?

Often leaders must make important decisions that affect many people and influence a whole culture. Sometimes the people agree with the leader. Sometimes not. This happened in ancient times as well. Read each of the following facts found in *Greece*. Decide whether you agree or disagree with the decision each person made. Explain your answer.

1. Solon, a popular politician, insisted that all laws be written down. These laws could not be changed easily and would apply equally to both the rich and the poor. Do you agree or disagree with Solon's decision about the laws?

   I ________________ with Solon because ______________________________

   ____

   ____

   ____

   ____

   ____

   ____

2. In 508 B.C., a politician named Cleisthenes divided the people into tribes based on politics rather than social position. This decreased the power of the aristocratic archons. Do you agree or disagree with Cleisthenes' decision to divide the people into tribes?

   I ________________ with Cleisthenes because ________________________

   ____

   ____

   ____

   ____

   ____

   ____

continued

Name ______________________________

Support or Oppose? *continued*

3. After the Greek victory over the Persians, Pericles took the money from the Delian League and hired the best architects and artists to rebuild the Acropolis. Do you agree or disagree with Pericles' decision to use Delian money to rebuild the Acropolis?

   I ________________ with Pericles because ______________________

   ____

   ____

   ____

   ____

   ____

   ____

◎ **One Step Further:** Is there a policy or decision that's been made by a leader in your community or country with which you strongly agree or disagree? Explain the decision and why you feel as you do.

____

____

____

____

____

____

____

____

____

____

____

Name ______________________________

The Main Events

Ancient Greek literature is hailed as some of the finest in history! You've heard of the *Iliad* and the *Odyssey*, epic poems written by Homer. You've also heard of fables written by Aesop, who lived in ancient Greece.

Check your school or local library for ancient Greek literature (either original or retold versions). Make an outline of the story you read. Remember, you should have at least two supporting details for each main idea.

Title

I. Main Idea ______________________________

a. Supporting detail ______________________________

____

____

b. Supporting detail ______________________________

____

____

II. Main Idea ______________________________

a. Supporting detail ______________________________

____

____

b. Supporting detail ______________________________

____

____

◎ **One Step Further:** Draw a picture of an important scene from your story.

A Taste of Greece

Prepare an ancient Greek potluck lunch! Read again about what the ancient Greeks ate. Then research other sources to learn more about Greek foods. You'll find that their diet was very similar to that of modern Greeks.

Research some popular Greek recipes. Here are some Web links for Greek recipes.

http://www.eatgreektonight.com

http://www.ellada.com/grarr15.html

You may also find great Greek recipes in cookbooks from the library.

Finally, create the right atmosphere for your classroom party. Dress like the ancient Greeks! Turn your classroom into a festival! Check out the following Web site for more information on ancient Greek lifestyles.

http://members.aol.com/Donnclass/Greeklife.html

◎ **One Step Further:** Invite another class to join your celebration. Share what you've learned about ancient Greece with your guests.

Name ______________________________

Project Ideas

Choose from the following project suggestions to show what you've learned about ancient Greece. You may want to work with a partner or in a small group. Share your finished project with your classmates.

- Research the architecture of ancient Greece and recreate an ancient building using creative materials. Be prepared to give details about your building—when it was built, why it was built, how it was used.
- Plato, Socrates, and Aristotle were often referred to as the "Great Thinkers." Many of their ideas about life led to debates among their peers. Think of a topic that affects your life, such as a school policy, a parent's rule, or even a government issue. Then write and present a persuasive speech on whether this is positive and should continue or negative and should be changed. Remember, don't be argumentative. Just present the issue and facts to support your view.
- Research the Greek alphabet. Create a poster showing a comparison with the English alphabet. Write a message to a friend using the Greek alphabet and challenge him or her to decipher it.
- The Minoan civilization may have come to an end as the result of a massive volcano eruption. Research other volcanic eruptions that occurred in ancient times such as those that destroyed Pompeii and the island of Thera. Devise a creative way to share your information with the class.
- Plan a virtual trip to modern-day Greece to visit some of the ancient sites. How will you travel? What will you visit? Where will you stay? Keep a journal that covers your trip. Use drawings or pictures from magazines or the Internet to enhance your journal text. Display your journal in the classroom.
- Write a humorous myth featuring one or more of the Greek gods and goddesses.
- Research to find out what life was like in various city-states in Greece, such as Sparta, Corinth, Argos, and Megara. Compare the lifestyles with those of the people in Athens. To get started, you might want to check the following Web site: **http://members.aol.com/Donnclass/Greeklife.html**.
- Make a poster or chart comparing the gods of the Greeks, the Romans, and the Vikings. Note the similarities and differences.
- Write a play about two people from different ancient cultures meeting for the first time. What would they want the other to know about their lives? Ask a classmate to help present the play to the rest of the class. Create costumes that are typical of each culture.
- Compare and contrast the ancient Greek Olympics with modern-day Olympics. Display your findings on a chart.

Name ______________________________

Twenty-Question Objective Test

Directions: Match each word and its meaning.

______	1. potsherd	a.	god, or something considered a god
______	2. frieze	b.	cruel, unfair ruler
______	3. deity	c.	wall carving
______	4. libation	d.	broken piece of pottery
______	5. tyrant	e.	beverage; drink

Directions: Answer each statement True (T) or False (F).

______ 6. Athena is the goddess of war and wisdom.

______ 7. The modern Olympics that we now see began in 1896.

______ 8. Today, Greeks write from right to left.

______ 9. The two most important fruit crops in ancient Greece were figs and carrots.

______ 10. A skene was a field for athletic competitions.

Directions: Choose the best answer to complete each statement.

11. Three cultures that developed during the Bronze Age were
    a. Athenian, Spartan, and Trojan.
    b. Cycladic, Minoan, and Mycenaean.
    c. Persian, Roman, and Macedonian.

12. King Minos was a
    a. legendary ruler of Crete.
    b. famous explorer and conqueror.
    c. cruel tyrant of Athens.

continued

Greece

Twenty-Question Objective Test continued

13. The Hellenistic Period began when
    a. Rome conquered Athens.
    b. Alexander the Great died.
    c. Solon came into power.

14. Troy was a great city in what is now
    a. Egypt.
    b. Turkey.
    c. Hungary.

15. The era of Pericles' leadership of Athens is often called the
    a. Dark Ages.
    b. period of confusion.
    c. Golden Age.

16. The agora was the
    a. central square of ancient Greek cities.
    b. Greek god of agriculture.
    c. Greek theater.

17. Pythagoras was a famous
    a. playwright.
    b. architect.
    c. mathematician.

18. Ancient Greek religion was based on
    a. myths.
    b. daily life.
    c. texts like the Old Testament.

19. For thousands of years, the center of the Greek world was the city of
    a. Athens.
    b. Troy.
    c. Sparta.

continued

Name ______________________

Greece

Twenty-Question Objective Test continued

Directions: Answer the question using complete sentences.

20. What was life like for girls and women in ancient Greece?

Rome
in Brief

Chapter 1 of *Rome* explores the fascinating history of this once-powerful metropolis. This city enjoyed great prosperity and growth for more than 1,000 years.

Ancient Rome had many similarities to modern-day cities. It swelled with beautiful buildings, including theaters, homes, arches, and temples. The Forum Romanum stood as the center of public life with its many shops, markets, and political and religious buildings.

In 410 A.D., the city of Rome was attacked by barbarians and partially destroyed. The Western Empire went into decline and finally fell in 476 A.D.

Chapter 2 unveils the religion of Rome. In early Roman history, worshipers believed that spirits inhabited the natural world in forms such as rocks, trees, and rivers. Later, Greek mythology was blended with stories of Roman gods. In turn, the gods of the Roman religions developed a more human form.

The Romans used rituals to communicate with their gods. These included animal sacrifices and obedience to strict customs and traditions. The Romans also built many colorful temples in which to honor and worship their gods.

Chapter 3 delves into the rich language of ancient Rome. The minor language of Latin eventually reached the corners of the Roman Empire and became its most common form of communication. The spoken form of Latin is the base from which the romance languages of French, Italian, Spanish, Portuguese, and Romanian have evolved.

The ancient Romans also loved to write. They left clues to their culture with Latin engravings on just about everything—tablets, monuments, gravestones, literature, and more.

Chapter 4 entertains us with stories of Roman games. Going to the chariot races and the theater were two of the most popular pastimes. Performances were scheduled at the theater more than 100 days a year.

Many Romans were also spectators of games such as gladiator contests and animal hunts. These took place in an amphitheater, a circular theater with stadium seating. Later on, the famous Colosseum was built, and it housed many of these contests.

Chapter 5 gives a taste of ancient Rome's favorite foods. Historians and archaeologists know what Romans ate through their studies of excavated ancient trash, food-related literature, and even paintings.

An ancient Roman lunch might have consisted of bread, fruit, and cheese. Dinners included vegetables, legumes, and possibly some meat.

Chapter 6 takes a look at how the Romans organized water flow in a remarkably intricate way. Through aqueducts, the Romans successfully channeled water into their homes, public baths, factories, and sewers.

Chapter 7 looks into the circumstances that left the commercial town of Pompeii in ruins. In August of 79 A.D., Mount Vesuvius erupted and destroyed Pompeii as well as the surrounding towns.

In the mid-18th century, the town was discovered completely preserved. Many historians and archaeologists have discovered much about ancient Roman life through excavations of Pompeii.

Reading Exploration Essentials

Vocabulary

amphitheater	archaeology	aristocratic	barbarian
Christianity	class	commemorated	converted
divination	dominant	Etruscan	execution
exotic	exported	fortress	governing body
hearth	imperial	imported	inscription
Judaism	lapilli	legume	lentil
Mediterranean	metropolis	molten	patron
persecuted	Renaissance	rituals	sacked
triumphal			

Reading Exploration

prereading

Find the modern city of Rome on a classroom map or globe. Explain to the students that this modern city has a rich history dating all the way back to 753 B.C. Ask them to look over the table of contents in *Rome*. Have them share which chapter they think looks the most interesting. Ask students to create a double-column list. In the left column, have them compose a list of questions they hope to have answered by the end of the study.

during reading

Have students fill in the right column with any answers they come across while reading.

As you come to Chapter 7 of *Rome*, display a map of Italy. Point out Mount Vesuvius and the modern city of Pompeii, which is about a mile away from where the ancient city of Pompeii was found.

Find the modern city of Ercolano, the city built on top of the ancient city of Herculaneum, also destroyed by Mount Vesuvius. Refer to these locations often as you read about and discuss the catastrophic event.

postreading

Ask students to reread their list of questions. Have students share any answers they found that were especially interesting. Encourage students to do more research on their chosen topic on the Internet or in the library. Challenge them to come back with one interesting fact that they think no one else in the class has heard before.

Name ______________________________

Show and Tell

Have you ever come across an unfamiliar word while reading? Of course!

Rarely does an author stop in the middle of a story to give a quick definition. Many times, however, the meaning of a new word is shown through helpful surrounding words, or context clues.

For example, read the following sentence.

I think *pastina* is far more delicious than the larger types of pasta found in soups.

Because of the context clues in this sentence, you now know all of the following about pastina.

- Pastina is a type of pasta.
- It is a small pasta.
- It is found in soup.
- According to the writer, it is delicious.

Read the following sentences. In the blank after each one, list what you know about the italicized vocabulary word just from the context clues. When you are finished, check the definition of the word in the glossary of *Rome*.

1. Joe wants to study *archaeology* in college because he has always been fascinated with fossils and artifacts.

   ____

   ____

   ____

2. The girl never married her true love as he was from a different *class* in their society.

   ____

   ____

   ____

3. The man discovered a Latin *inscription* written on a stone.

   ____

   ____

   ____

continued

Name ______________________________

Show and Tell *continued*

4. We knew by her generous donations to the museum that she was a *patron* of the arts.

____

____

____

5. The once-powerful *metropolis* of Rome had similarities to modern-day cities.

____

____

____

6. Thousands of Romans gathered in the *amphitheater* to watch games and sporting events in ancient Rome.

____

____

____

◎ **One Step Further:** Make up your own sentences below that contain context clues. Use the glossary in *Rome* for help.

1. lapilli ______________________________

____

Clues: Show that lapilli is from a volcano. Show that it is hot or destructive.

2. lentil ______________________________

____

Clues: Show that the lentil is a vegetable. Show that it is small.

Name ______________________________

Why?

Throughout time, events have occurred with results that changed history. Read the following passage. Then think about what happened and why it happened.

The busy port of ancient Pompeii sat right on the Bay of Naples. It was a center for exporting as well as importing to other ports on the Mediterranean Sea. Some people in the city became very rich. They showed off their wealth by building beautiful houses and decorating them with fountains, pools, statues, mosaics, and paintings.

On August 24, 79 A.D., the volcano Mount Vesuvius erupted. Thousands of people lost their homes, possessions, pets, and even their lives. After 20 hours of lapilli, or pumice, and ash falling from the sky, the city of Pompeii was completely buried.

Archaeologists know much of what happened on that day because of the eyewitness account of Pliny the Younger. He wrote a letter to his friend, the great historian Tacitus, who was looking for information about the eruption.

Choose the best answer to complete each statement.

1. Pompeii was a center for exporting and importing because
   a. it was an ancient city.
   b. it was located near the water.
   c. it was near Mount Vesuvius.
2. People built beautiful houses and decorated them because
   a. they were rich.
   b. they wanted to please the gods.
   c. they knew they were going to die soon.
3. Thousands lost everything including their lives because
   a. Pompeii sat right on the Bay of Naples.
   b. lapilli and ash buried the city when the volcano erupted.
   c. they had spent everything on their homes.
4. Tacitus was able to write a historical account of the eruption because
   a. archaeologists had an eyewitness account of the incident.
   b. he had been in Pompeii when the volcano erupted.
   c. Pliny the Younger wrote him a letter detailing what happened.

continued

Name ____________________

Why? *continued*

◎ **One Step Further:** Think about what you read in *Rome*. Write five sentences that show cause and effect—a happening and why it happened.

1. ____________________

____

2. ____________________

____

3. ____________________

____

4. ____________________

____

5. ____________________

____

Name ______________________________

It's a Fact!

A fact is a proven or definite truth. An opinion is one person's perspective or feelings about something. You can find both facts and opinions in all types of literature. For example, a newspaper is a great source for facts. Yet you can also find personal opinions on many subjects in the newspaper, especially in the editorial section.

Rome is full of interesting facts about Rome as well as the culture of its citizens.

Read each of the following facts below. Then give a possible opinion from an ancient Roman's point of view.

Example: **Fact:** Surrounding the city was an 11-mile-long wall built in 270 A.D. by the Emperor Aurelian.

Opinion: That wall is so inconvenient.

1. **Fact:** In 410 A.D., the city of Rome was sacked and partially destroyed by barbarian invaders.

   Opinion: ______________________________

   ____

2. **Fact:** Vergil's *Aeneid* is a long poem that traces the history of Rome from its legendary founding up to the time of the Emperor Augustus.

   Opinion: ______________________________

   ____

3. **Fact:** In gladiatorial contests, pairs of men would fight in hand-to-hand combat.

   Opinion: ______________________________

   ____

continued

It's a Fact! *continued*

4. **Fact:** Archaeologists study real garbage from ancient times recovered from excavations all over the world.

   Opinion: ____________________

   ____

5. **Fact:** Most people went to public baths located around the city.

   Opinion: ____________________

   ____

6. **Fact:** The Forum Romanum was the center of public life with its shops, markets, and political buildings.

   Opinion: ____________________

   ____

Name ______________________________

Remember Me

Imagine that you are a resident of Pompeii in 79 A.D., the year that Mount Vesuvius erupted. You and your family escape with your lives, but many of your belongings have to be left behind.

A few months later, you decide that you want your story to be told, so you write a letter to the people of the future. In the letter, tell the following.

- Who you are
- When you first noticed something was wrong
- What you did
- How you managed to escape
- The sights, smells, and sounds around you

Don't forget to use the parts of a letter, such as the heading, salutation, body, closing, and your signature.

Name ______________________________

Et Tu, Brute?

A favorite Roman activity was going to the theater. Performances were scheduled more than 100 days a year. Read again about the Roman theater in Chapter 4 of *Rome*.

Now gather four or five classmates and write a short play, or skit, with an ancient Roman theme. Work together to come up with an interesting plot, characters, and setting. Decide if you will have a narrator and who it will be. Assign characters. Create very simple costumes and props. Practice your lines and perform your play for the rest of your class!

Organize your thoughts below.

Name of Play ______________________________

Actors (List actors' real names and stage names)

______________________ as ______________________

______________________ as ______________________

______________________ as ______________________

______________________ as ______________________

______________________ as ______________________

Setting ______________________________

Story ______________________________

____

◎ **One Step Further:** Do you think you would have wanted to be an actor or a spectator if you lived in ancient Roman times? Explain your answer.

____

____

____

____

____

____

Name ____________________

Project Ideas

Choose from the following project suggestions to show what you've learned about ancient Rome. You may want to work with a partner or in a small group. Share your finished project with your classmates.

- Many English words have Latin roots. Research Latin root words at your local library or on the Internet. Choose at least five Latin roots and list as many English words as you can that come from them. Compare your list with those of your classmates. Here is a Web site that you might find useful. **http://www.knownet.net/users/Ackley/vocabroot.html**

- We still use Roman numerals today. You have seen them in every day things such as clocks and chapter titles. Imagine, however, having to use only Roman numerals every day as the ancient Romans did! Read again about Roman numerals in Chapter 3 of *Rome*. Then figure out how to write the following numbers Roman-style: your age, the year you will graduate, your address, and the current year. Create five math problems with Roman numerals to share with your classmates.

- Romans enjoyed watching mimes based on everyday life. Think of something you do often (do homework, watch TV, play soccer, etc). Act it out in a mime in front of your classmates and challenge them to guess what you're doing.

- Draw a map of Italy on a large posterboard. Include all of the major cities found in *Rome*. Be creative.

- The Romans are famous for their magnificent buildings. Do further research on one of these famous structures listed in *Rome*, and create an original model. Use any materials you'd like.

- Read again what kinds of foods were grown and eaten in ancient Rome. Using one or more of these foods as the main ingredient, create a tasty dish to share with your class.

- Write a poem about how it feels to be emperor of Rome.

- The great Theater of Marcellus held as many as 15,000 spectators. Research some of the theaters or stadiums in your area. How do they compare with the Theater of Marcellus? Record your findings on a graph.

- The ancient Romans developed intricate water systems. Using small pipes or straws, create your own water system demonstrating how gravity can make water flow along a chosen path.

- Mount Vesuvius affected the lives of about 20,000 residents in Pompeii. Research more about today's active volcanoes. Are any in danger of erupting? Who would be affected? Record your findings in a brief report.

Name ____

Twenty-Question Objective Test

Directions: Match each word and its meaning.

______ 1. Christianity	a.	period of European history between the 14th and 17th centuries
______ 2. Etruscan	b.	inhabitant of ancient Etruria, a country that was in western Italy
______ 3. Renaissance	c.	religion based on Jesus Christ and his teachings
______ 4. divination	d.	central area of the home
______ 5. hearth	e.	interpretation of messages sent by the gods

---

Directions: Answer each statement True (T) or False (F).

______ 6. Rome's most important public space was the Forum Romanum.

______ 7. In 410 A.D., the city of Rome was partially destroyed by barbarians.

______ 8. Ancient Romans worshiped only one god.

______ 9. The main language of ancient Rome was Romanian.

______ 10. Ancient Romans could see chariot races at the Circus Maximus.

Directions: Choose the best answer to complete each statement.

11. Legend has it that in the year 753 B.C.
    a. Romulus founded the city of Rome on top of Palatine Hill.
    b. the gods constructed the first building in Rome.
    c. Remus fell into a deep sleep and dreamed of what Rome would become.

12. Roman temples were
    a. solid white.
    b. light blue with solid gold corners.
    c. brightly painted with blue, green, red, black, and gold paints.

continued

Name ______________________________

Rome

Twenty-Question Objective Test continued

13. Virgil's *Aeneid* is a
    a. long poem that traces the history of Rome.
    b. famous play that was performed only for wealthy citizens.
    c. monument built for the emperor.

14. The Roman numeral XV is
    a. 5.
    b. 15.
    c. 20.

15. The favorite pastime of ancient Romans was
    a. worshiping in Roman temples.
    b. writing plays.
    c. going to the chariot races.

16. The best-known entertainment center in ancient Rome is the
    a. Colosseum.
    b. Pantheon.
    c. Aqua Appia.

17. Mount Vesuvius erupted in
    a. 24 A.D.
    b. 48 A.D.
    c. 79 A.D.

18. We know much about the eruption of Mount Vesuvius from the firsthand account of
    a. Caesar.
    b. Pliny the Younger.
    c. Tacitus.

19. The Western Roman Empire ended in
    a. 476 A.D.
    b. 890 A.D.
    c. 1010 A.D.

continued

Rome

Twenty-Question Objective Test continued

Directions: Answer the question using complete sentences.

20. How was ancient Roman life like life today?

The Vikings in Brief

Chapter 1 of *The Vikings* introduces these ancient conquerors and gives insight into their past culture and society. Archaeologists study ancient Viking artifacts, bones, and even soil to figure out what crops the Vikings grew and what materials they used in their building projects. Ancient shops have been discovered, as well as pieces of metal, glass, gold, whale ivory, amber, and more. The Vikings are known to have been expert craftsmen and active traders.

Chapter 2 emphasizes the reasons behind the rampages and conquests of the Scandinavian Vikings. During the Dark Ages, Europe was already a hostile place in which rulers conquered other lands in violent raids.

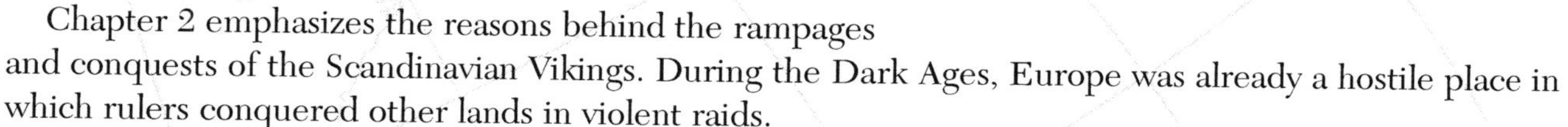

As their population grew, the Vikings needed more territory and didn't mind taking risks and exploring new lands. They were successful in their raids, conquering many lands and acquiring new riches. The Vikings invaded many European countries in the 8th and 9th centuries. They were greatly feared by the people of England, Ireland, France, and Russia.

Chapter 3 focuses on two of the most famous Vikings, Erik the Red and his son, Leif Erikson. After being banished from Iceland for murder, Erik the Red decided to go exploring. He discovered a new land, which he called Greenland. He eventually returned to Iceland. There, he convinced hundreds of people to move to Greenland.

Erik the Red's son, Leif Erikson, was an honest and fair man who had a strong urge for travel and exploration. He discovered new lands, including Newfoundland. Once he rescued a crew from their wrecked trading vessel and was given the entire rich cargo as a reward. He was then nicknamed Leif the Lucky.

Chapter 4 emphasizes the spectacular shipbuilding skills of the Vikings. They built advanced ships that gave them a clear advantage in their voyages and as a result, had a strong, positive impact on their trade, politics, warfare, and exploration endeavors.

The two most common ships were the drekar, a fast and flexible ship, and the knarr, an ocean-going cargo vessel. Archaeologists have figured out the ages of ancient Viking ships through dendochronology, the practice of tree-ring dating.

Chapter 5 reveals the different religions practiced by the Vikings. Like other ancient cultures, the Vikings worshiped numerous gods and goddesses. Several days of the week are named after Viking gods. While almost the entire Scandinavian population was pagan at the beginning of the Viking Age, many Vikings came to accept Christianity as it was introduced to them in their newly conquered lands.

Chapter 6 explores the written symbols and language of the Vikings. Each of their written symbols, called runes, represented both a sound and a meaning. Runes were also believed to have magical properties. Rune Masters were trained to use runes to heal the sick, protect warriors in battle, and answer questions.

Old Norse was the spoken language of the Vikings. This language influenced the dialects in other lands, especially England. Many everyday English words have Scandinavian roots.

Reading Exploration Essentials

Vocabulary

abbey	artifact	banish	bounty
bow	chiefdom	daub	deity
devout	dialect	divination	drekar
estate	Etruscan	excavation	exploits
feldspar	infamous	Inuit	knarr
Northumbria	pagan	pillaged	polarize
rampaged	Rus Viking	ruthless	sacked
seaworthy	stereotype	stern	surname
Vinland			

Reading Exploration

prereading

Display a world map. Point out the countries where the Viking culture began—Norway, Denmark, and Sweden. Present the Vikings as explorers and conquerors who lived in a violent and hostile time period.

during reading

As students read about the many conquests and explorations of the Vikings, ask them to identify each new land on the map. This will be especially relevant in Chapter 1, as it relates how Viking groups spread to particular areas and countries.

Have students find the city of Yorkshire in northern England where the Jorvik archaeological site is located.

As students read Chapter 3, follow the explorations of Erik the Red and Leif Erikson on the map as well.

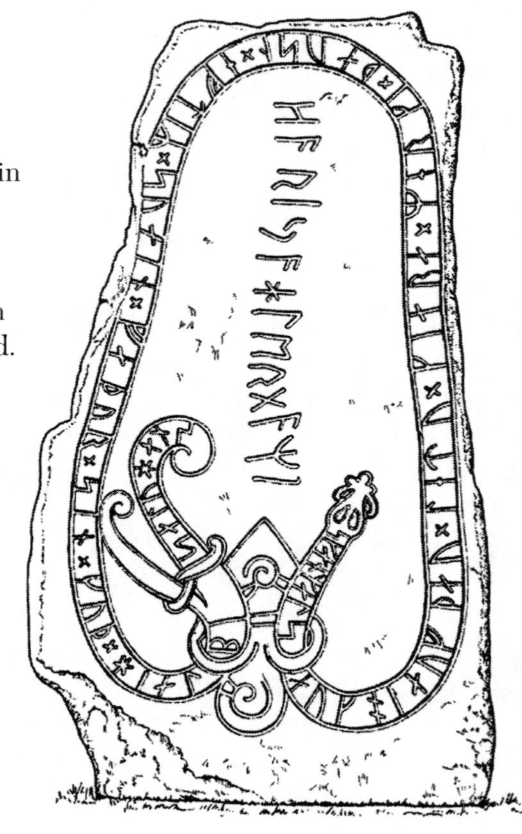

postreading

After reading *The Vikings*, use the following discussion questions.

- Compare Viking ships with ships today.
- How did the Vikings influence other cultures and languages?
- Would you like to have lived during this time period? Why or why not?

Name ______________________________

A Viking Dictionary

You're the editor of the new Viking dictionary! Alphabetize the following Viking vocabulary words on the pages below. Guide words are given for each of the four pages. Write a definition in your own words for each alphabetized word. Use the glossary in *The Vikings* for help.

ruthless	knarr	chiefdom	feldspar
dialect	pagan	estate	bounty
banish	drekar	abbey	daub

abandon • bunt

1. ______________________

definition: ______________________

2. ______________________

definition: ______________________

3. ______________________

definition: ______________________

drawn • keep

7. ______________________

definition: ______________________

8. ______________________

definition: ______________________

9. ______________________

definition: ______________________

butter • diamond

4. ______________________

definition: ______________________

5. ______________________

definition: ______________________

6. ______________________

definition: ______________________

knapsack • rye

10. ______________________

definition: ______________________

11. ______________________

definition: ______________________

12. ______________________

definition: ______________________

continued

Name ________________________________

A Viking Dictionary *continued*

◎ **One Step Further:** Choose additional interesting words from *The Vikings* that you want to remember. Write them on the lines below. Look up each word in a dictionary and write a definition in your own words.

word: ____________________

definition: ____________________

____

word: ____________________

definition: ____________________

____

word: ____________________

definition: ____________________

____

word: ____________________

definition: ____________________

____

word: ____________________

definition: ____________________

____

word: ____________________

definition: ____________________

____

word: ____________________

definition: ____________________

____

word: ____________________

definition: ____________________

____

Name ______________________________

What If . . . ?

History explains events from the past. But what if one part of an event had happened differently? What might have been the consequences or outcomes? Read each "What If" question below. Decide how history might have changed, and record your response on the lines provided.

1. What if the Vikings had been satisfied with their settlements in Sweden, Denmark, and Norway and had not explored lands to the east and west? ______________

   ____

   ____

2. What if the Vikings had been peace-loving, friendly people instead of hostile, fearsome warriors? ______________________________

   ____

   ____

3. What if Thorfinn Karlsefni and the 600 people he took to the New World had survived the winter famine and Indian attacks? ______________

   ____

   ____

4. What if the Vikings had not been such great shipbuilders? ______________

   ____

   ____

5. What if the Vikings had never developed the Runic alphabet? ______________

   ____

   ____

◎ **One Step Further:** Write a "What If" question and have your classmates respond to it.

____

____

Name ______________________________

Recycled Information

If you were to tell a friend about a topic you read in *The Vikings*, you wouldn't need to recall every single fact. Summarizing skills would come in handy. Look over the topics listed below. Read about them again in *The Vikings*, and try to remember some details about each one. On the lines below each topic, write down some of the important details that would summarize what you read.

- The Jorvik Archaeological Site

  ____

  ____

- Viking Women and Children

  ____

  ____

- Eric Bloodaxe

  ____

  ____

- Tree-Ring Dating

  ____

  ____

- The Runic Alphabet

  ____

  ____

◎ **One Step Further:** Prepare a short speech using one of the summaries. Record your speech or present it to the class.

Name ______________________________

A Viking Saga

Many cultures have a rich history of folklore and tall tales that are exaggerated stories of either real or fictitious people. Some American tall tales include Johnny Appleseed and Paul Bunyan.

A saga is the tale of a historic or legendary event in Norway or Iceland. Read again about either Erik the Red or Leif Erikson. Write a tale based on one of these explorers. You can make it a tall tale (exaggerate it) or keep it based on historic facts. Begin by recording notes below.

What would be a good setting? What kinds of characters and conflicts would make a really interesting story? What must your hero or heroine overcome? Who is the villain and what is his/her purpose in the story? Skim through *The Vikings* for good ideas.

Ideas for settings

____

____

____

Ideas for characters

____

____

____

Plot

____

____

____

Share your ideas with one or two other classmates. Listen to their ideas. Does someone have a great setting while someone else has terrific characters? Work together to come up with the best story you can. Then get started. You may write one story together or work separately and see what you each come up with!

◎ **One Step Further:** Illustrate your tale and display it in the media center for other classes to enjoy.

Name ________________________________

Greenland Is Ice and Iceland Is Nice

The Vikings lived, explored, and conquered in frigid climates. This must have posed unique challenges as they established new settlements.

After Erik the Red told of the bounty he found in Greenland, hundreds of Icelanders left to see for themselves. They would eventually find that their original home of Iceland had a greener, milder climate than Greenland, which was mostly covered in ice!

It's been said that the Vikings made up the name "Greenland" to make others want to move there, leaving Iceland for themselves!

See for yourself! Choose both a northern and southern city from both Iceland and Greenland. Use the Internet, an almanac, or an encyclopedia to find their average winter and summer temperatures and then record them in the chart below.

A map of Iceland can be found at **www.lib.utexas.edu/maps/europe/iceland.gif** and a map of Greenland can be found at **www.greeland-guide.dk/gt/maps/default.htm**.

Country	Cities	Average Winter Temps	Average Summer Temps
Iceland	____________	________	________
Greenland	____________	________	________

- Which country and city have the coldest winters? ________________________________

  ____

- Which country and city have the warmest summers? ________________________________

  ____

- Why do you think the climates are so different? ________________________________

  ____

One Step Further: Make a map of the North Atlantic Ocean. Show Canada, Greenland, Iceland, and the Scandinavian countries. Mark the Arctic Circle. Add other features that you find interesting. Indicate the cities listed in your chart. Display the map and a copy of your chart in the classroom.

Name ______________________________

Project Ideas

Choose from the following project suggestions to show what you've learned about the Vikings. You may want to work with a partner or in a small group. Share your finished project with your classmates.

- The suffix *-by* means "homestead" or "village." The English towns of Grimsby and Derby were originally Viking settlements. Create and name an imaginary town using the suffix *-by*. Make a map of your city and explain how you came up with its name. For example: Roseby—village of roses!
- Think of questions you would like to ask a dendochronologist. Then arrange an interview with one of these scientists. If this is not possible, research to find the answers to your questions. Present your interview to the class. Ask a classmate to ask your questions. Pretend you're the dendochronologist as you provide the answers.
- Design a word search using the vocabulary words in *The Vikings*. Challenge your classmates to solve it.
- Thorfinn Karlsefni set out for the New World with three boats carrying 600 men, women, and cattle. Make a chart showing four different ways in which they could have divided up the 600 passengers into the three boats. Explain which, in your opinion, would have been the safest and most comfortable?
- Write and present a speech from Erik the Red's point of view as he tried to persuade people to settle in Greenland.
- Research either the drekar or the knarr, the two most common Viking ships. Create a model using creative materials. Visit these Internet sites for great information on Viking ships.
  www.pbs.org/wgbh/nova/vikings/ships.html
  www.stemnet.nf.ca/CITE/vikingships.htm
- Create a map tracking the Vikings' conquests. Use different colors to represent the different voyages and conquests. Be sure to include a key!
- Create a large illustrated timeline of the major events in Viking history.
- Choose an animal that lives in Scandinavia and write a short report. How has it adapted to its climate? Explain where and how the Vikings might have come in contact with this animal?
- Research the Viking gods. Make an illustrated chart listing the gods by order of importance. Also show their relationships to one another. Share your chart with your classmates.

Name ____________________________________

Twenty-Question Objective Test

Directions: Match each word to its meaning.

______	1. Futhark	a. longship
______	2. pagan	b. Runic alphabet
______	3. drekar	c. ocean-going cargo vessel
______	4. knarr	d. follower of a religion with many gods
______	5. Skraelings	e. the ugly men

Directions: Answer each statement True (T) or False (F).

______ 6. The Vikings thrived a long time in North America.

______ 7. Sagas were stories of Norse history and legend written in the 12th and 13th centuries.

______ 8. Wealthy Viking warriors were buried with their valuable possessions.

______ 9. Dendochronologists study tree rings in order to date wood.

______ 10. Thor was the god of death and war.

Directions: Choose the best answer to complete each statement.

11. Viking culture began in Scandinavia in the countries now called
    a. Newfoundland and Greenland.
    b. Iceland, France, and Spain.
    c. Norway, Denmark, and Sweden.

12. Viking women
    a. were expert shipbuilders.
    b. managed the farms while the men were away.
    c. fought alongside the men.

continued

Name ______________________________

The Vikings

Twenty-Question Objective Test continued

13. Erik the Red was banished from Iceland for
    a. theft.
    b. murder.
    c. treason.

14. After arriving in Norway, Leif Erikson became a
    a. Christian.
    b. Pagan.
    c. Buddhist.

15. Vikings considered their gods as
    a. perfect and all-knowing.
    b. all evil.
    c. having humanlike qualities.

16. The Vikings believed their gods lived in place called
    a. Iceland.
    b. Olympus.
    c. Asgard.

17. Tiu, the Viking god of war and battles, was missing a/an
    a. leg.
    b. hand.
    c. eye.

18. The word *rune* means
    a. "trick."
    b. "magic spell or whisper."
    c. "hieroglyphics."

19. The English language is a combination of
    a. Latin, Old Norse, Old English, and French.
    b. Old Norse, French, and Italian.
    c. Latin, Old English, Afrikaans, and Greek.

continued

Name ______________________________

The Vikings

Twenty-Question Objective Test continued

Directions: Answer the question using complete sentences.

20. Why was life so difficult for the Vikings living in the New World?

Answer Key

China

Ancient Chinese Secrets (page 17)
1. dynasty/c; 2. Huns/e; 3. irrigation/a; 4. nomad/d; 5. legacy/b; 6. artisan/f

Rich Man, Poor Man (page 18)

	Poor	Wealthy
Diets	ate simple meals consisting of rice, grains, some vegetables, beans; occasionally chicken, birds, or fish; used spices, soy sauce, and honey.	diets more varied including pork, lamb, duck, goose, pigeon, venison as well as fresh fruits and vegetables; ate snakes, snails, sparrows, or bear claws on special occasions; used spices, soy sauce, and honey.
Clothing	wore long shirts of woven hemp; little or no jewelry; crude sandals.	fine silk clothing; jewelry of gold, jade, and other semiprecious stones.
Housing	cooked outside; shared communal toilet and bath.	private kitchens and bathrooms

Chinese Fiction (page 19)
Responses will vary.

A Second Chance (page 20)
Responses will vary.

An Invention That Counts (page 21)
Responses will vary.

Twenty-Question Objective Test: China (page 23)
1. c; 2. a; 3. e; 4. b; 5. d; 6. F; 7. T; 8. T; 9. F; 10. F; 11. b; 12. a; 13. b; 14. c; 15. a; 16. b; 17. a; 18. c; 19. a; 20. Responses will vary but may include: The nobility disliked Shihuangdi because he deprived them of their power. The common people hated his heavy taxation, harsh laws, and heavy work projects. Intellectuals disliked him because he banned all books except those that flattered him or dealt with his favorite topics. He killed people that disagreed with him.

Egypt

The Whole Story (page 28)
1. Nile River; 2. stele; 3. hieroglyphics; 4. mummy; 5. pharaoh; 6. sarcophagus; 7. canopic jar; 8. archaeologist; 9. Egyptologist

continued

Extra! Extra! Read All About It! (page 29)
Responses will vary.

The Memory of an Elephant (page 30)
Responses will vary slightly but should include the following ideas:
1. The ancient Egyptians enjoyed foods such as melons, figs, pomegranates, onions, beans, garlic, eggs, bread, fish, and occasionally meat. 2. Hieroglyphics is the Egyptian language made of picture signs and symbols. 3. Egyptian children played with toys such as model animals, dolls, tops, and clay balls. 4. The ancient Egyptians built the pyramids to be used as burial places for the pharaohs. 5. King Tut became king at age nine.

Actions Speak Louder Than Being Verbs (page 31)
Responses will vary.

Build a Pyramid (page 32)
Projects will vary.

Twenty-Question Objective Test: Egypt (page 34)
1. b; 2. a; 3. d; 4. c; 5. e; 6. F; 7. T; 8. F; 9. T; 10. T; 11. b; 12. a; 13. b; 14. c;
15. c; 16. a; 17. b; 18. a; 19. b; 20. Responses will vary but may include the following:
The pyramids are considered amazing because they were built at a time when people didn't possess today's knowledge of math, science, or technology.

Greece

Word Exchange (page 39)
Responses will vary but may include the following: 1. bond/union/relationship; 2. area/region/territory; 3. noblemen/rulers; 4. legendary/heroic; 5. decode/translate/interpret; 6. main/major/prevailing; 7. craftsmen/experts; 8. relics/remnants; 9. plundered/destroyed/robbed; 10. protected/secure/strong

History in a Nutshell (page 41)
1. 431 B.C.; 2. 550 B.C.; 3. 3000–1400 B.C.; 4. 478 B.C.; 5. 338 B.C.; 6. about 525 B.C.; 7. 560 B.C.; 8. 1183 B.C.; 9. 146 B.C.; 10. 776 B.C.; 11. 508 B.C.; 12. about 2000 B.C.; 13. 1000 B.C.; 14. 490 B. C.; 15. 447 B. C.

Bronze Age 3000–1200 B.C.	Dark Ages 1200–750 B.C	Archaic Period 750–500 B.C.	Classical Period 500–323 B.C.	Hellenistic Period 323–31 B.C.
3; 12	8; 10; 13	2; 6; 7; 11	1; 4; 5; 14; 15	9

Support or Oppose (page 43)
Responses will vary.

continued

The Main Events (page 45)
Responses will vary.

A Taste of Greece (page 46)
Recipes will vary.

Twenty-Question Objective Test: Greece (page 48)
1. d; 2. c; 3. a; 4. e; 5. b; 6. T; 7. T; 8. F; 9. F; 10. F; 11. b; 12. a; 13. b; 14. b; 15. c; 16. a; 17. c; 18. a; 19. a; 20. Responses will vary but should include the following: Female children stayed at home to learn to care for the house and family. Only the wealthiest girls may have studied with an in-house tutor. All Greek women learned to spin yarn and weave cloth. Only girls from Sparta could exercise in public. Girls usually married at age 14 or 15 to a man chosen by their father. Women were not permitted to vote.

Rome

Show and Tell (page 53)
Responses will vary, but may include the following. 1. Archaeology is a type of study. It has to do with ancient relics like fossils and artifacts. 2. Class separates people. It occurs in society. It is discriminating. 3. An inscription can be done in a language; it can be engraved on something hard like a rock. 4. A patron supports a cause. 5. A metropolis must be the same as a city. 6. An amphitheater must be big. It must be a place to sit and watch games, like a stadium.

Why? (page 55)
1. b; 2. a; 3. b; 4. c

It's a Fact! (page 57)
Responses will vary.

Remember Me (page 59)
Responses will vary.

Et Tu, Brute? (page 60)
Responses will vary.

Twenty-Question Objective Test: Rome (page 62)
1. c; 2. b; 3. a; 4. e; 5. d; 6. T; 7. T; 8. F; 9. F; 10. T; 11. a; 12. c; 13. a; 14. b; 15. c; 16. a; 17. c; 18. b; 19. a; 20. Responses will vary but may include the following: The ancient Romans had heated and running water; malls; a fire station; large, solid buildings; and a lot of entertainment!

continued

The Vikings

A Viking Dictionary (page 67)
1. abbey; 2. banish; 3. bounty; 4. chiefdom; 5. daub; 6. dialect; 7. drekar; 8. estate; 9. feldspar; 10. knarr; 11. pagan; 12. ruthless. Definitions will vary but should be close to the glossary definition.

What If . . . ? (page 69)
Responses will vary.

Recycled Information (page 70)
Responses will vary.

A Viking Saga (page 71)
Responses will vary.

Greenland Is Ice and Iceland Is Nice (page 72)
Responses will vary.

Twenty-Question Objective Test: The Vikings (page 74)
1. b; 2. d; 3. a; 4. c; 5. e; 6. F; 7. T; 8. T; 9. T; 10. F; 11. c; 12. b; 13. b; 14. a; 15. c; 16. c; 17. b; 18. b; 19. a; 20. Responses will vary but may include the following: The Vikings faced a winter famine, conflicts with Indians, and experienced tension between the Christians and pagans.